HOCKEY STARS

2023/24 SEASON

coloring book

sportz@artcreations.online

You can download the jersey color guide in a high definition PDF for free by following this link.

TEAM
Chicago Blackhawks

FOUNDED	CONFERENCE	DIVISION
1.926	Western	Central

CITY	ARENA	CAPACITY
Chicago (Illinois)	United Center	19.717

CONNOR BEDARD

TEAM		
Colorado Avalanche		

FOUNDED	CONFERENCE	DIVISION
1.972	Western	Central

CITY	ARENA	CAPACITY
Denver (Colorado)	Ball Arena	17.809

NATHAN MACKINNON
BAUER
BAUER

TEAM		
Columbus Blue Jackets		

FOUNDED	CONFERENCE	DIVISION
2.000	Eastern	Metropolitan

CITY	ARENA	CAPACITY
Columbus (Ohio)	Nationwide Arena	18.144

BOONE JENNER

TEAM
Dallas Stars

FOUNDED	CONFERENCE	DIVISION
1.967	Western	Central

CITY	ARENA	CAPACITY
Dallas (Texas)	American Airlines Cen-ter	18.532

JAKE OETTINGER
29
BAUER
SUPREME

TEAM		
Detroit Red Wings		

FOUNDED	CONFERENCE	DIVISION
1.926	Eastern	Atlantic

CITY	ARENA	CAPACITY
Detroit (Michigan)	Little Caesars Arena	19.515

ALEX DEBRINCAT
93
CCM
93
BAUER
SHERWOOD

TEAM		
Edmonton Oilers		

FOUNDED	CONFERENCE	DIVISION
1.972	Western	Pacific

CITY	ARENA	CAPACITY
Edmonton (Alberta)	Rogers Place	18.347

CONNOR MCDAVID
97
CCM

TEAM
Florida Panthers

FOUNDED	CONFERENCE	DIVISION
1.993	Eastern	Atlantic

CITY	ARENA	CAPACITY
Sunrise (Florida)	Amerant Bank Arena	19.250

SAM REINHART

TEAM		
Los Angeles Kings		

FOUNDED	CONFERENCE	DIVISION
1.967	Western	Pacific

CITY	ARENA	CAPACITY
Los Angeles (California)	Crypto.com Arena	18.230

CAM TALBOT
LA
BAUER
BAUER
BAUER
BAUER
BAUER

TEAM
Minnesota Wild

FOUNDED	CONFERENCE	DIVISION
2.000	Western	Central

CITY	ARENA	CAPACITY
Saint Paul (Minnesota)	Xcel Energy Center	17.954

KIRILL KAPRIZOV

TEAM		
Montreal Canadiens		

FOUNDED	CONFERENCE	DIVISION
1.909	Eastern	Atlantic

CITY	ARENA	CAPACITY
Montreal (Quebec)	Bell Centre	21.105

NICK SUZUKI

TEAM		
Nashville Predators		

FOUNDED	CONFERENCE	DIVISION
1.998	Western	Central

CITY	ARENA	CAPACITY
Nashville (Tennessee)	Bridgestone Arena	17.159

FILIP FORSBERG

TEAM		
New Jersey Devils		

FOUNDED	CONFERENCE	DIVISION
1.974	Eastern	Metropolitan

CITY	ARENA	CAPACITY
Newark (New Jersey)	Prudential Center	16.514

JACK HUGHES
86
BAUER
RWJBarnabas HEALTH
86
A

TEAM		
New York Islanders		

FOUNDED	CONFERENCE	DIVISION
1.972	Eastern	Metropolitan

CITY	ARENA	CAPACITY
Elmont (New York)	UBS Arena	17.255

MATHEW BARZAL

TEAM
New York Rangers

FOUNDED	CONFERENCE	DIVISION
1.926	Eastern	Metropolitan

CITY	ARENA	CAPACITY
New York City (New York)	Madison Square Garden	18.006

IGOR SHESTERKIN
10
CCM

TEAM		
Ottawa Senators		

FOUNDED	CONFERENCE	DIVISION
1.992	Eastern	Atlantic

CITY	ARENA	CAPACITY
Ottawa (Ontario)	Canadian Tire Centre	19.347

BRADY TKACHUK
CIBC
C
TRUE
TRUE

TEAM		
Pittsburgh Penguins		

FOUNDED	CONFERENCE	DIVISION
1.967	Eastern	Metropolitan

CITY	ARENA	CAPACITY
Pittsburgh (Pennsylva-nia)	PPG Paints Arena	18.387

SIDNEY CROSBY
87
CCM
F.N.B
C
87
87
PENGUINS
CCM
87
CM
PENGUINS

TEAM		
San Jose Sharks		

FOUNDED	CONFERENCE	DIVISION
1.991	Western	Pacific

CITY	ARENA	CAPACITY
San Jose (California)	SAP Center	17.562

TOMAS HERTL
48
CCM
SAP

TEAM		
Seattle Kraken		

FOUNDED	CONFERENCE	DIVISION
2.021	Western	Pacific

CITY	ARENA	CAPACITY
Seattle (Washington)	Climate Pledge Arena	17.151

OLIVER BJORKSTRAND

TEAM		
St. Louis Blues		

FOUNDED	CONFERENCE	DIVISION
1.967	Western	Central

CITY	ARENA	CAPACITY
St. Louis (Missouri)	Enterprise Center	18.724

ROBERT THOMAS

TEAM
Tampa Bay Lightning

FOUNDED	CONFERENCE	DIVISION
1.992	Eastern	Atlantic

CITY	ARENA	CAPACITY
Tampa (Florida)	Amalie Arena	19.092

NIKITA KUCHEROV
86
BAUER
A
86

TEAM		
Toronto Maple Leafs		

FOUNDED	CONFERENCE	DIVISION
1.917	Eastern	Atlantic

CITY	ARENA	CAPACITY
Toronto (Ontario)	Scotiabank Arena	18.819

AUSTON MATTHEWS

TEAM		
Vancouver Canucks		

FOUNDED	CONFERENCE	DIVISION
1.945	Western	Pacific

CITY	ARENA	CAPACITY
Vancouver (British Columbia)	Rogers Arena	18.910

QUINN HUGHES
43
BAUER
C
43

TEAM		
Washington Capitals		

FOUNDED	CONFERENCE	DIVISION
1.974	Eastern	Metropolitan

CITY	ARENA	CAPACITY
Washington (D.C.)	Capital One Arena	18.573

TOM WILSON
43
Bauer
43
WASHINGTON
Bauer

TEAM
Winnipeg Jets

FOUNDED	CONFERENCE	DIVISION
1.999	Western	Central

CITY	ARENA	CAPACITY
Winnipeg (Manitoba)	Canada Life Centre	15.321

CONNOR HELLEBUYCK

TEAM
Anaheim Ducks

FOUNDED	CONFERENCE	DIVISION
1.993	Western	Pacific

CITY	ARENA	CAPACITY
Anaheim (California)	Honda Center	17.174

FRANK VATRANO
77
CCM
bauer
BAUER

TEAM		
Arizona Coyotes		

FOUNDED	CONFERENCE	DIVISION
1.972	Western	Central

CITY	ARENA	CAPACITY
Tempe (Arizona)	Mullett Arena	4.600

CLAYTON KELLER
CCM
BAUER
CCM

TEAM
Boston Bruins

FOUNDED	CONFERENCE	DIVISION
1.924	Eastern	Atlantic

CITY	ARENA	CAPACITY
Boston (Massachusetts)	TD Garden	17.850

DAVID PASTRNAK

TEAM		
Buffalo Sabres		

FOUNDED	CONFERENCE	DIVISION
1.970	Eastern	Atlantic

CITY	ARENA	CAPACITY
Buffalo (New York)	KeyBank Center	19.070

RASMUS DAHLIN

TEAM		
Calgary Flames		

FOUNDED	CONFERENCE	DIVISION
1.972	Western	Pacific

CITY	ARENA	CAPACITY
Calgary (Alberta)	Scotiabank Saddledome	19.289

ELIAS LINDHOLM
28
A
RIOR
CCM

TEAM		
Carolina Hurricanes		

FOUNDED	CONFERENCE	DIVISION
1.972	Eastern	Metropolitan

CITY	ARENA	CAPACITY
Raleigh (North Carolina)	PNC Arena	18.680

SEBASTIAN AHO
CCM
5

TEAM
Philadelphia Flyers

FOUNDED	CONFERENCE	DIVISION
1.967	Eastern	Metropolitan

CITY	ARENA	CAPACITY
Philadelphia (Pennsylva-nia)	Wells Fargo Center	19.500

TRAVIS KONECNY

TEAM		
Vegas Golden Knights		

FOUNDED	CONFERENCE	DIVISION
2.017	Western	Pacific

CITY	ARENA	CAPACITY
Paradise (Nevada)	T-Mobile Arena	17.500

JACK EICHEL
Circa
SPORTS
9

I hope you enjoyed the book.
If you liked it, leave us a nice review on Amazon and your comments so we can keep improving!

We really appreciate your input and will be happy to implement your recommendations.

Made in United States
Troutdale, OR
09/03/2024